Chris Buckton
Anne Sanderson

Series editor:
Leonie Bennett

Photocopy Masters

Differentiation and Homework

Author Team: Chris Buckton
Anne Sanderson
Series Editor: Leonie Bennett

Ginn
Linacre House, Jordan Hill, Oxford, OX2 8DP
a division of Reed Educational and Professional Publishing Ltd
www.ginn.co.uk

ISBN 0602 296870

04 03 02 01
10 9 8 7 6 5 4 3 2

Designed by Gecko Ltd, Bicester, Oxon
Cover design by Gecko Ltd, Bicester, Oxon
Printed in the UK by Ashford Colour Press, Hampshire

Acknowledgements
The publisher would like to thank the following for permission to reproduce their copyright material:
PCMs 8/9: from *Fantastic Mr Fox: A Play* by Roald Dahl and Sally Reid (Penguin Books Ltd) reproduced by permission of David Higham Associates Ltd; **PCM 10**: from *Fantastic Mr Fox* by Roald Dahl (Penguin Books Ltd), reproduced by permission of David Higham Associates Ltd; **PCM 32**: from *The Iron Woman* by Ted Hughes (Faber & Faber Ltd), reproduced by permission of Faber & Faber Ltd; **PCM 38**: 'Henry King' by Hilaire Belloc from *Cautionary Verses* (Random House UK Ltd) © The Estate of Hilaire Belloc, reproduced by permission of Peters, Fraser and Dunlop Group Ltd on behalf of the Estate; **PCM 44**: text from *Mr Creep the Crook* by Allan Ahlberg, illustrated by Andre Amstutz (Viking, 1998) text © Allan Ahlberg, 1998, reproduced by permission of Penguin Books Ltd; **PCM 59**: from 'Return to Air' in *What the Neighbours Did and Other Stories* by Philippa Pearce (Puffin, 1975) © Philippa Pearce 1964, 1969, 1972, reproduced by permission of Penguin Books Ltd.

Contents

1 Photocopy Masters for differentiation and homework

2 Prompt Charts

3 OHT Correlation Chart

4 Photocopy Masters of OHTs

NAME ______________________ DATE ____________

Read the character sketch below. Then complete the sentences.

It was a horrible sight. It was only about two metres high, with short thick legs, but its body was large, like a rock. Its skin was green and warty. On the top of its head were spikes of fiery red hair. It looked very mean. And it smelt terrible.

We think the character is a ______________________

because ______________________

We think it looked mean because ______________________

____

A body like a rock is ______________________

We think the creature might smell of ______________________

____

NAME ________________________________ DATE ______________

Read the character sketch below. Then complete the sentences.

He was tall, thin and very old, with long white hair and a beard that reached down to his waist. He was wearing red velvet robes embroidered with silver moons and stars, and a tall pointed hat that sat at a slight angle on his head. His face was warm and kind, and his grey eyes twinkled when he smiled. In his left hand he carried a long ebony cane, and if you looked very closely you could see that the little finger of the hand was missing.

1 We think the character is a __________________ because ___________

____

2 We think the character is sympathetic/unsympathetic.

Choose 3 **adjectives** which make you think that.

____

3 We think the story might be about ______________________________

____

4 We think he might have lost his finger when _____________________

____

5 One word to describe him would be ____________________________

NAME ______________________ DATE ____________

Adjectives and Verbs

1 Think of three **ADJECTIVES** you could use to describe a **thin** person.

2 Think of three **ADJECTIVES** you could use to describe a **kind** person.

3 Think of three **VERBS** to describe how somebody **moved**:

e.g. strolled, bounced

4 Think of three **VERBS** to describe how somebody **spoke**:

e.g. shouted, cried

NAME ______________________ DATE ____________

Movement?

Sympathetic

Thin or fat?

Young or old?

Unsympathetic

Face?

Hair?

Clothes?

Voice?

My description: ______________________

____

____

NAME ______________________ DATE ____________

QUESTIONNAIRE

Working with a Partner

1 What do you find most helpful when you are planning?

- (a) brainstorming
- (b) just talking
- (c) using a planning sheet

2 What do you find helpful when you're in the middle of writing?

- (a) reading bits of your work aloud to your partner
- (b) asking your partner to read the first bit to themselves
- (c) just asking for help if you get stuck

3 What do you like your partner to do when you've written a first draft?

- (a) only tell you good things
- (b) tell you good things and then say where you could improve it
- (c) only tell you what's wrong

4 What do you like your partner to do when you've finished?

5 Finish this sentence.

A good response partner is someone who

Any other comments

NAME ______________________ DATE ____________

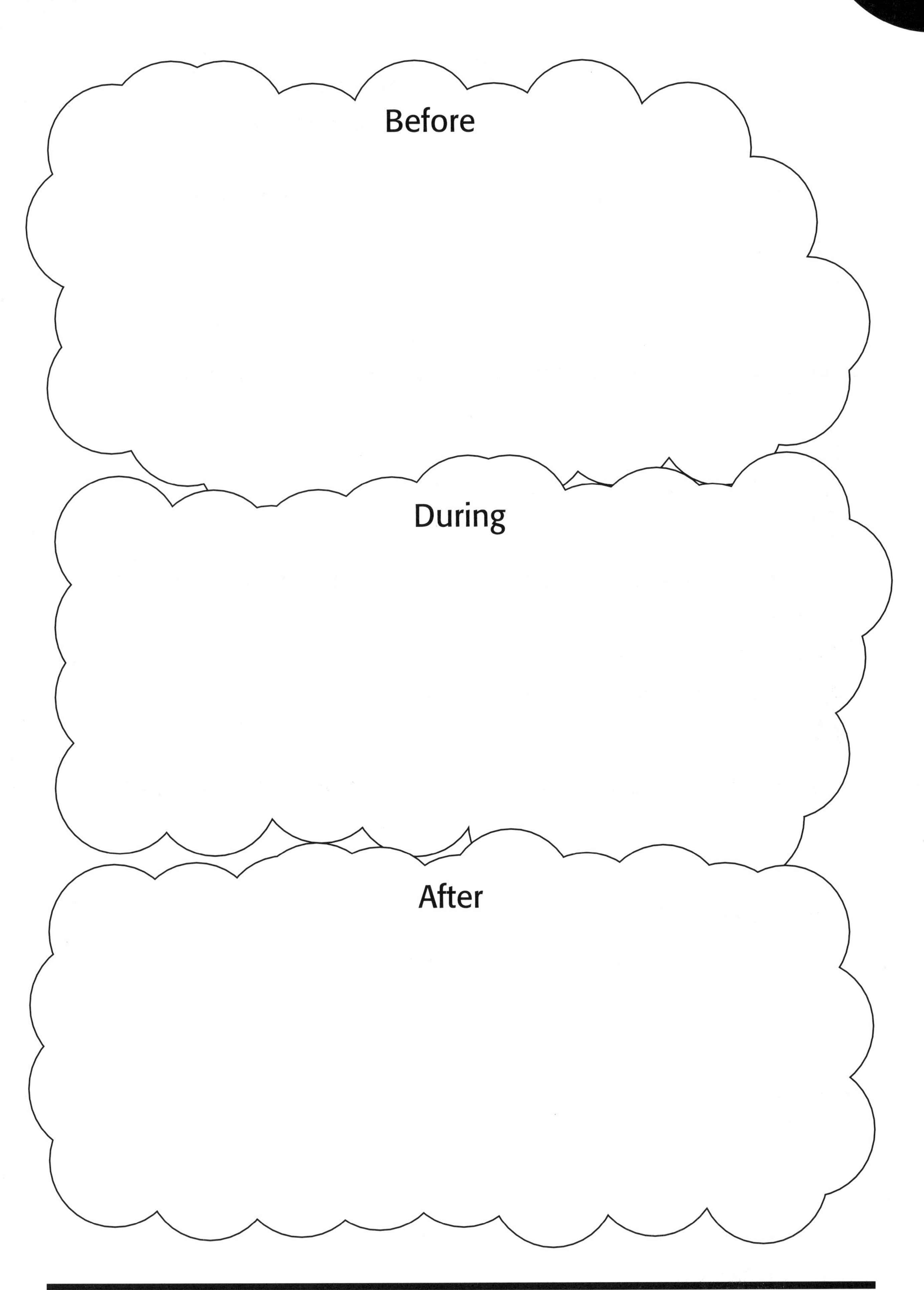

NAME ______________________________ DATE ______________

Introduction

Build-up

Climax

Resolution

NAME ________________________________ DATE ____________

Scene 1

BOGGIS, BUNCE and BEAN *are seated at three tables laden with food and placed in a line on stage in front of the drawn curtains. They are 'frozen'. Children enter from the back of the hall (spotlight). They skip, run and laugh up the centre aisle, chanting:*

Children: Boggis and Bunce and Bean,
One fat, one short, one lean,
These horrible crooks,
So different in looks,
Were none the less equally mean.

(Children sit on steps at front of stage. As each farmer is mentioned, a spotlight pans on to him and he becomes alive, eating or drinking revoltingly.)

First child: Let's sit down a minute.

Second child: What shall we do? We could go up to the woods and play.

Third child: Or we could go down to the river.

First child: Better not. My mum says I'm not to go anywhere near the valley 'cos of those three nasty men. You know the ones – they're always talking together in low whispers and looking over their shoulders to see if anyone's listening. The dreaded Boggis, Bunce and Bean, no less.

Second child: My mum says the same. She says not only are they the nastiest farmers in the whole county, they're also the richest. They never spend any money and they pay miserable wages to everyone who works for them. They store all the money they get from selling their chickens and ducks and geese in great padlocked chests.

Third child: Which do you think is the worst?

Second child: Don't know. They've all got such horrible habits. (*Laughter*)

NAME ______________________________ DATE ____________

Fantastic Mr Fox Scene 1 continued . . .

First child: I think old Boggis is the worst. (*Spotlight on BOGGIS*) He's got absolutely thousands of chickens locked away in those chicken houses. And he's so *fat*. He's got a head like the top of a boiled egg and a bristly, greasy moustache. D'you know, he eats three boiled chickens smothered with dumplings every day for breakfast, lunch and supper? I can just see him eating the chicken legs in his fingers and all the grease getting in his moustache and running down his chin.

Children: Ugh!

Second child: What about that pot-bellied dwarf Bunce then? (*Spotlight on BUNCE*) He keeps thousands of ducks and geese. He lives on doughnuts and goose livers. He mashes the livers into a disgusting paste and then stuffs the paste into the doughnuts. It gives him such a tummy ache he's always in a foul temper. You should see his kitchen – it's filthy, and the stench hits you even before you open the door.

Third child: Ah, but I don't believe there can be anyone more disgusting or more revolting [illegible] n *BEAN*) He's the one that kee[illegible] turkeys in that orchard full o[illegible] Boggis is fat – but what's mc[illegible] f them all. He doesn't eat any [illegible] lons of strong cider made from al[illegible] ver washes. His earholes are clo[illegible] ck and wax and bits of chewing [illegible]

Write down six words to describe BOGGIS:

Write down six words to describe BUNCE:

Write down six words to describe BEAN:

NAME ______________________________ DATE ____________

1 Using different colours, underline the words said by: Mr Fox, Bunce, Boggis and Bean. Look for clues that tell you *how* the lines could be spoken.

2 Put a box round the words that tell you where the scene takes place (setting).

3 Put a wavy line, ﹏﹏﹏ under words which tell the actors what to do.

Chapter 2

On a hill above the valley there was a wood.

In the wood there was a huge tree.

Under the tree there was a hole.

In the hole lived Mr Fox and Mrs Fox and their four small foxes.

Every evening as soon as it got dark, Mr Fox would say to Mrs Fox, 'Well, my darling, what shall it be this time? A plump chicken from Boggis? A duck or a goose from Bunce? Or a nice turkey from Bean?' And when Mrs Fox had told him what she wanted, Mr Fox would creep down into the darkness of the night and help himself.

Boggis and Bunce and Bean knew very well what was going on, and it made them wild with rage...

'Dang and blast that lousy beast!' cried Boggis.

'I'd like to rip his guts out!' said Bunce.

'He must be killed!' cried Bean.

'But how?' said Boggis. 'How on earth can we watch the blighter?'

Bean picked his nose delicately with a long finger. 'I have a plan,' he said.

'You've never had a decent plan yet,' said Bunce.

'Shut up and listen,' said Bean. 'Tomorrow night we will all hide just outside the hole where the fox lives. We will wait there until he comes out. Then . . . *Bang! Bang-bang-bang*.'

NAME ______________________ DATE ____________

Fantastic Mr Fox: A Play

Scene ____________

On one side of the stage ______________________

______________________ *and on the other side*

____

Mr Fox (____________): ______________________

____

Mrs Fox: ______________________

(*Mr Fox crept* ______________________)

Boggis (____________): ______________________

Bunce (____________): ______________________

Bean (____________): ______________________

Boggis: ______________________

(*Bean* ______________________)

Bean: ______________________

Bunce (____________): ______________________

Bean (____________): ______________________

____

____

NAME ______________________ DATE ____________

1. Tick the items you might see in a newspaper report.

headline	☐	… the end.	☐
Once upon a time …	☐	paragraphs	☐
columns	☐	pictures	☐
speech	☐	photographs	☐

2. Imagine you are interviewing Farmer Bean.
What questions would you ask?

3. 'Feathers fly on local farms'
Write this headline as an ordinary sentence.

NAME ______________________________ DATE ______________

Some of the commas and speech marks are missing in this report.
Can you put them in?

FEATHERS FLY ON LOCAL FARMS

By Rashid Patel

Police are investigating a series of attacks on three poultry farms in the area.

According to local farmers Boggis Bunce and Bean the thief is almost certainly a cunning fox that lives above the valley in a wood. So far attempts to catch the thief have failed in spite of the farmers setting traps to catch him.

Farmer Bunce today told our reporter If I catch that fox, I'll put a bullet through his head. This seems to be the feeling of the other two farmers in the area.

Farmer Bean is setting up a Fox Watch, and is appealing to local residents to come and help. Anybody wishing to join should call 324447 as soon as possible.

NAME ______________________ DATE ____________

Headline

BRAINSTORM – FACTS

What?

When?

Where?

Who was involved?

QUOTES

NAME ______________________ DATE ____________

NAME ______________________________ DATE ____________

Choose words from the box below to describe how each of these characters acts and feels. List the words under each child's name. Write some more adjectives of your own.

William

The evacuee

Molly

miserable	kind	mischievous	
embarrassed	unkind	scared	angry
scornful	sorry		

NAME ______________________ DATE ____________

Imagine you are the evacuee. How would you feel? What would you do? Fill in the chart below.

What happened?	How you would have felt?	What you would have done?
The evacuees arrived from Liverpool, with labels tied to their coats.		
A small boy with a sharp nose and red eyes is the last one to be given a home.		
All the children laughed when he said, ‘You don’t get milk from cows. It comes in clean bottles.’		

NAME ______________________ DATE ____________

LEAVING HOME

When I knew I had to leave home, and go and live in a safe place in the country, I felt ______________________

First of all I ______________________

Then I ______________________

When we got to the country I ______________________

____

____

We had to wait until somebody took us home with them and I was the last one to be chosen. I felt ______________________

____

Everything was okay until this kid started to tease me. I ____________

____

Then when the others started laughing I ______________________

____

I felt ______________ and ______________

NAME ______________________ DATE ____________

1 Read the second part of the extract on page 18.

2 What is each paragraph about? Write a short caption saying what happened. Use your own words. Write in the past tense.

An example has been done for you

Paragraph 8

Philip sneaked out of the back of the house.

Paragraph 9

Paragraph 10

Paragraph 11

Paragraph 12

NAME ______________________________ DATE ____________

1 Put a verb into each of these sentences. Make sure you use the right tense!

a Philip's dad had ________________ him not to play with the kite.

b "It will ________________________ you away," said his mother.

c He heard a voice ____________________ inside his head, telling

him to take the kite outside.

d He ________________________ down the stairs as quietly as

he ____________________________ .

e The wind __________________________ the kite up in to the air.

2 Write out a sentence using each of the verbs below. Put each one into a different sentence. Underline the verb.

see **saw**

go **went**

can **could**

e.g. The old man came out to see what was going on.

The old woman saw that there was a fire in the woods.

NAME ______________________________ DATE ______________

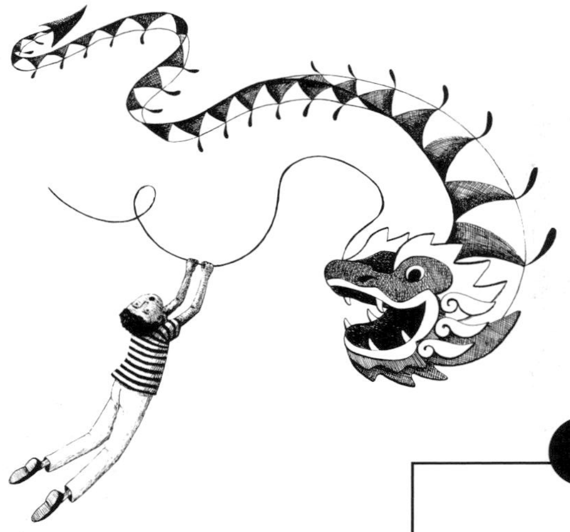

Paragraph 6

Paragraph 5

Paragraph 4

Paragraph 3

Paragraph 2

Paragraph 1

. . . He watched the top of the hill grow smaller and smaller until it was just a green dot below.

NAME ______________________________ DATE ______________

Make notes about an animal that you know well. It could be a family pet, or an animal you know a lot about.

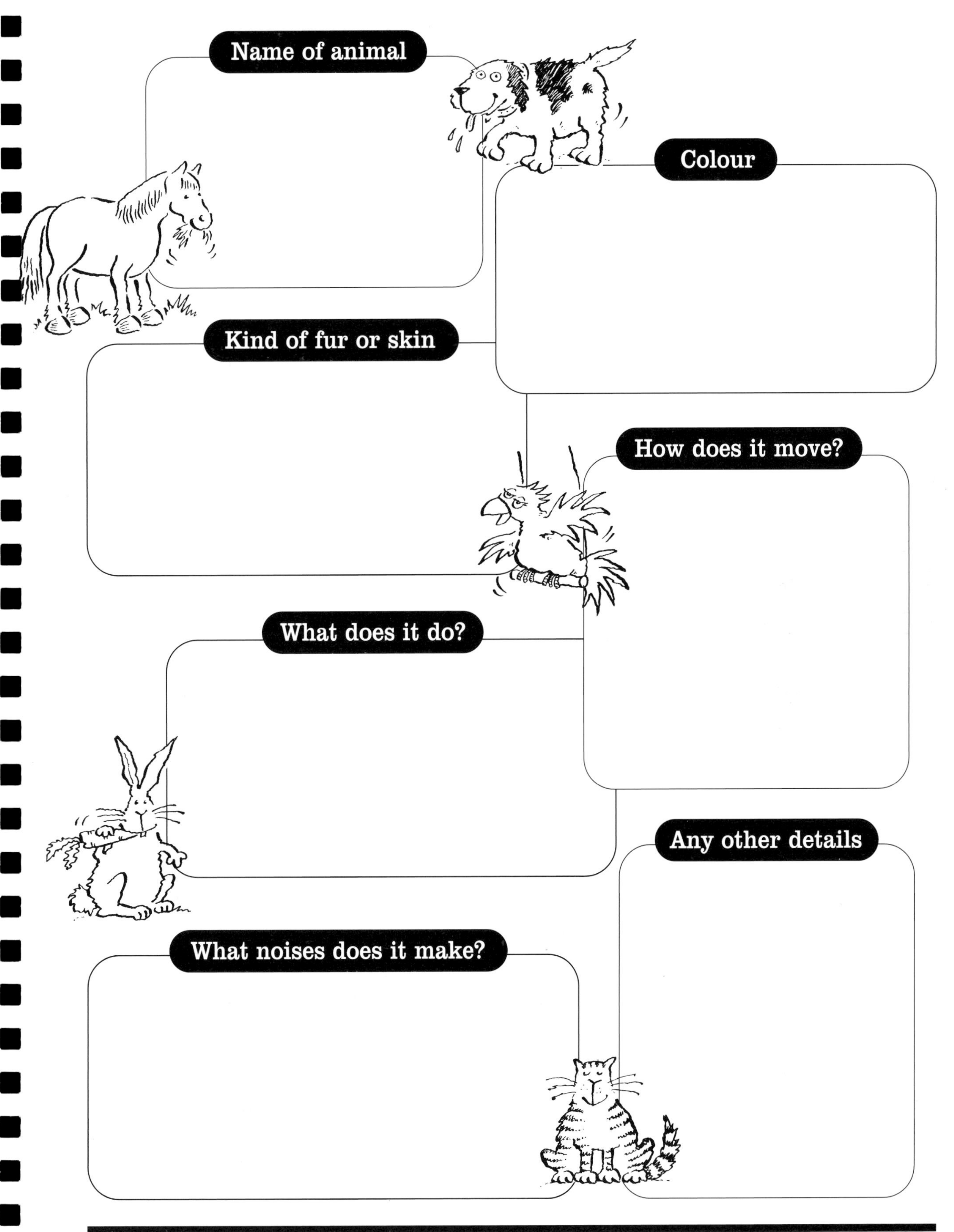

NAME ______________________________ DATE ______________

I see a ______________________________

______________________________ (What is it doing?)

______________________________ (How is it moving?)

______________________________ (What colour is it?)

______________________________ (What shape is its body?)

______________________________ (What is its skin or fur like?)

______________________________ (What noise does it make?)

______________________________ (What else does it do?)

______________________________ (Good closing line)

NAME ______________________ DATE ____________

Title of report ______________________

Paragraph 1: Introduction

Paragraph 2:

Paragraph 3:

Paragraph 4:

Paragraph 5: Summary

NAME ______________________ DATE ____________

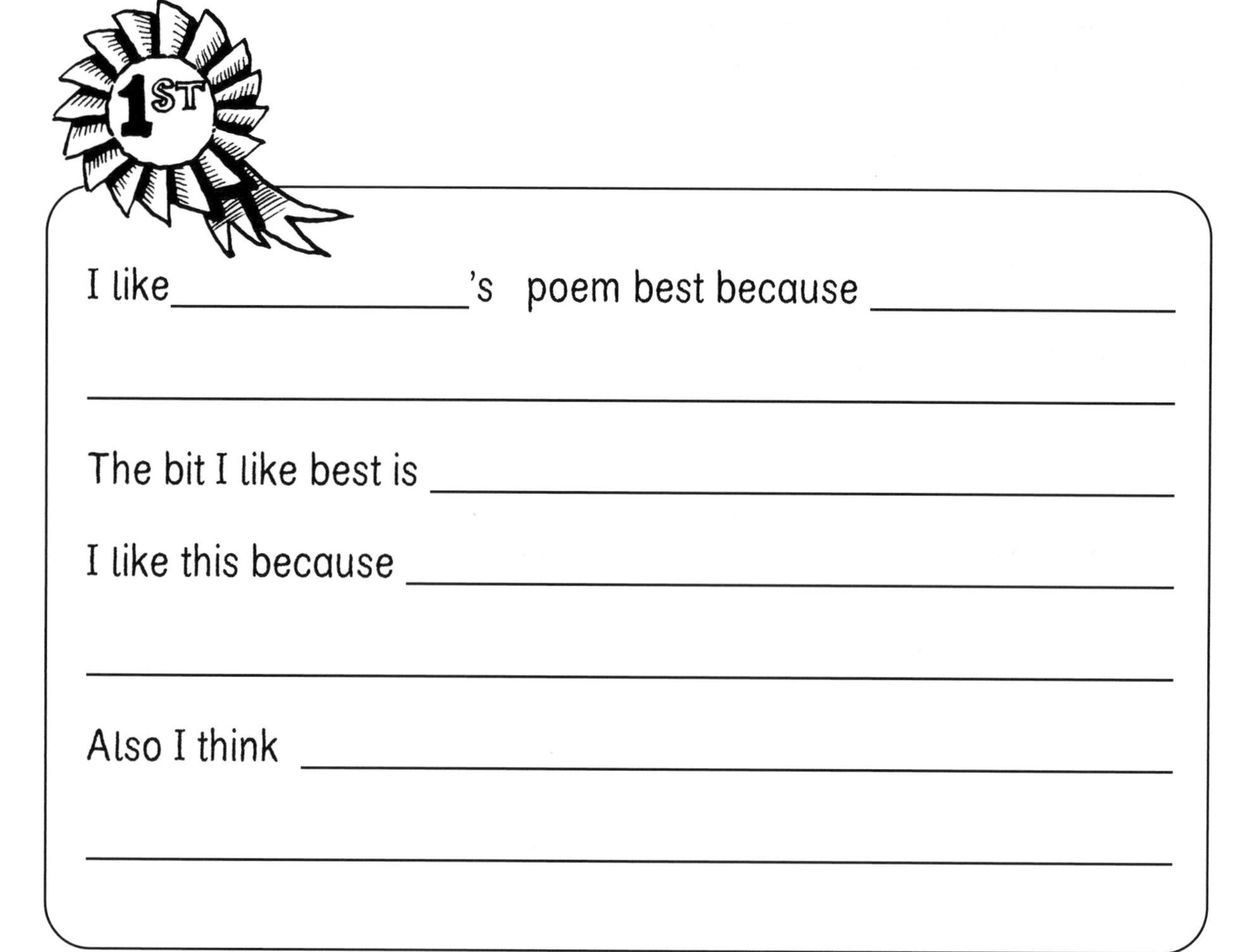

I like ______________'s poem best because ______________

____

The bit I like best is ______________________________

I like this because ________________________________

____

Also I think ______________________________________

____

I put ______________'s poem second because ______________

____

I don't think it's quite as good as ______________________'s

because ____

____

NAME ________________ DATE ________

1 Think of an adverb to 'add to the verb' in each of these sentences.
The first one has been done for you.

The bird flies swiftly

The dog jumps ________________

The cat purrs ________________

The lion pounces ________________

The horse gallops ________________

The cow walks ________________

2 Change the ending of each of these verbs to *-ing*. Watch out for tricky spellings!
Then add an adverb to describe the verb.
The first one has been done for you.

Run	Running	Running quickly
Roar		
Skip		
Waddle		
Flutter		
Slide		
Gallop		
Wriggle		

NAME ______________________ DATE ____________

Writing frame 1

I have a ______________________ in me

(verb) ______________ ing **(adverb)** ______________ ly

(adverb) ______________ ly **(verb)** ______________ ing

(adverb) ______________ **(verb)** ______________

(verb) ______________ **(adverb)** ______________

(how do people react?) ______________________

____

(how does your animal feel about this?) ______________

____

Writing frame 2

I have a ______________________ in me

It ______________ and ______________

It ______________ and ______________

It ______________ and ______________

It ______________ and ______________

People want to ______________________

NAME ______________________ DATE ____________

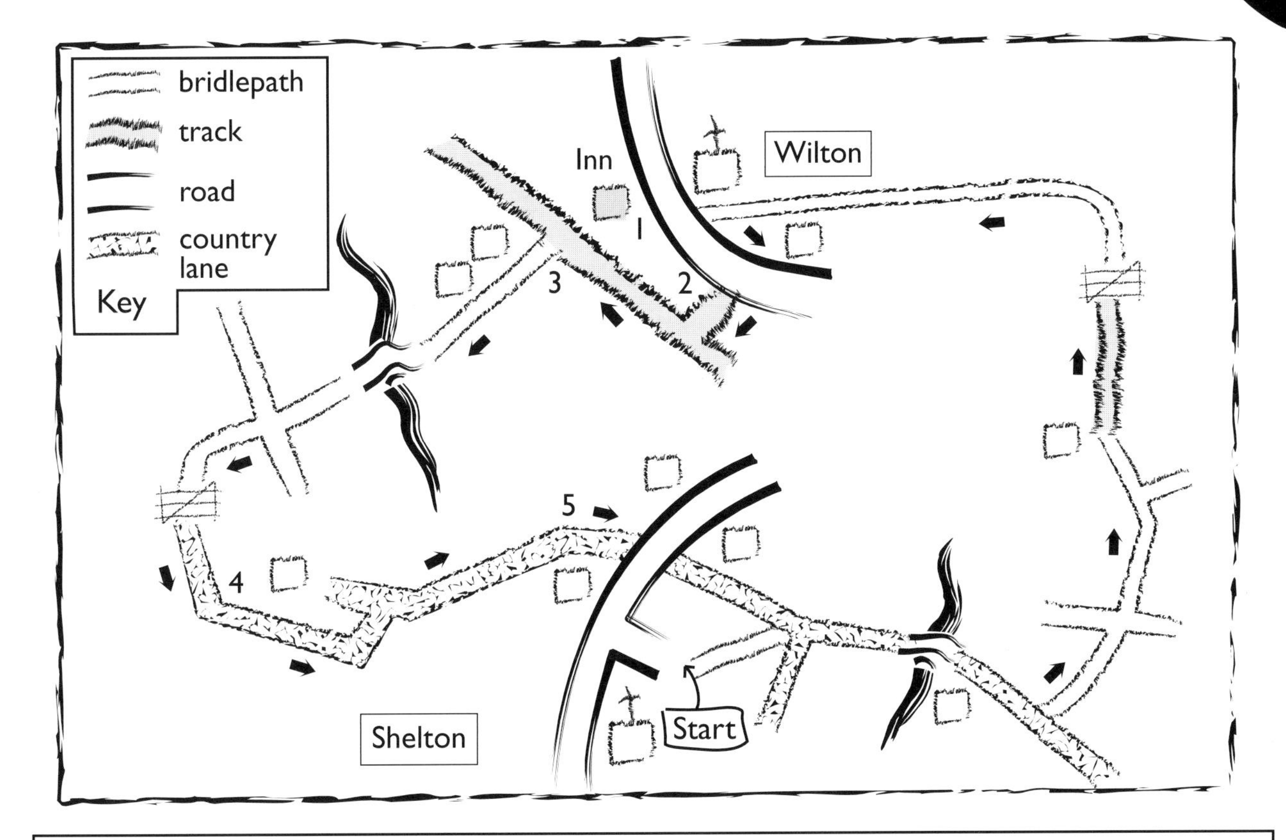

Words you might need

track	**left**	**right**	**gate**	**bridge**	**church**
houses	**lane**	**bridlepath**	**road**	**path**	

1 Come out of the inn at Wilton and turn ____________. Go down the ____________.

2 Turn ____________ on to a ____________. Turn ____________ again.

3 Go ____________ down the ____________ and over the ____________. Go through a ____________.

4 Go along the ____________. Turn ____________ and then follow the ____________ until you get to three ____________.

5 When you get to the ____________, turn ____________ to get back to the ____________.

NAME ______________________________ DATE ______________

What do these map symbols stand for?

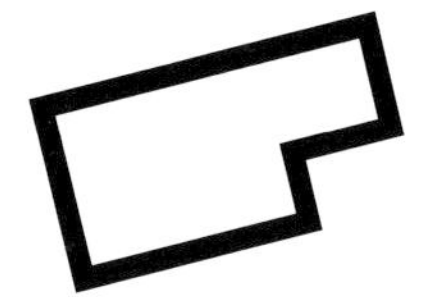

NAME ______________________________ DATE ____________

Work with a partner.

Read lines 1–24. Then tick the best answers. Use a dictionary to help you.

1 Lucy was frightened because the marsh was

a) dangerous

b) lonely

c) dark

2 Lucy thought it was an earthquake when

a) the birds flew away

b) she saw the reeds leaning all one way

c) the bridge road jumped

3 Lucy was standing

a) under the bridge

b) on the bridge

c) in the marsh

How do you know? Write down your evidence.

____

4 Complete this sentence:

The bit we like best is ______________________

____

because ______________________________________

____

 DATE ____________

Work with a partner.

Read through the extract again. Then answer the questions below.

1 'The water surface was blurred by a sudden mesh of tiny ripples.'

What was the water doing here?

What does mesh look like?

How would the water be 'blurred'?

2 'An earthquake! It must be an earthquake.'

Why does Lucy think it's an earthquake? Find the evidence in the text.

Why do you think these two short sentences are on a line by themselves?

3 What was worse than the bridge collapsing?

4 Choose your favourite bit of the story and practise reading it aloud. Write a sentence to say why you like it.

NAME ______________________ DATE ____________

The Iron Woman (continued)

Already the head was out. It still didn't look much like a head – simply a gigantic black lump, crowned with reeds and streaming with mud. But the mouth was clear, and after that first wailing cry the lips moved slowly, like a crab's, spitting out mud and roots.

Half an hour passed before the lump moved again. As it moved, the reeds away to either side of it bulged upwards and heaved, and the black watery mud streamed through them. The mouth opened and a long booming groan came out of it, as the head hoisted clear. Another groan became a wailing roar. A seagull blowing across the marsh like a paper scrap veered wildly upwards as the streaming shape reared in front of it, like a sudden wall of a cliff, pouring cataracts of black mud, and clotted, rooty lumps of reeds where grass snakes squirmed and water voles flailed their forepaws, blinking their eyes and squealing as they fell.

The black shape was the size of two or three elephants. It looked like a hippopotamus-headed, gigantic dinosaur, dragging itself on all fours up out of a prehistoric tar pit. But now, still like a dinosaur, it sat upright. And all at once it looked human – immense but human. Great hands clawed at the head, flinging away squatches of muddy reeds. Then, amid the gurglings and suckings, and with a groaning wail, the thing stood erect. A truly colossal, man-shaped statue of black mud, raking itself and groaning, towered over the marsh.

NAME ______________________ DATE ____________

I was walking ______________________

____

I looked at the ______________________

I could hear ______________________

Suddenly ______________________!

I saw ______________________

It was ______________________

Its head ______________________

Its body ______________________

Its hands ______________________

I felt ______________________

For a few seconds I ______________________

Then I began to ______________________

____

____

NAME ______________________ DATE ____________

Label this diagram of a vacuum cleaner. Explain to your partner how it works.

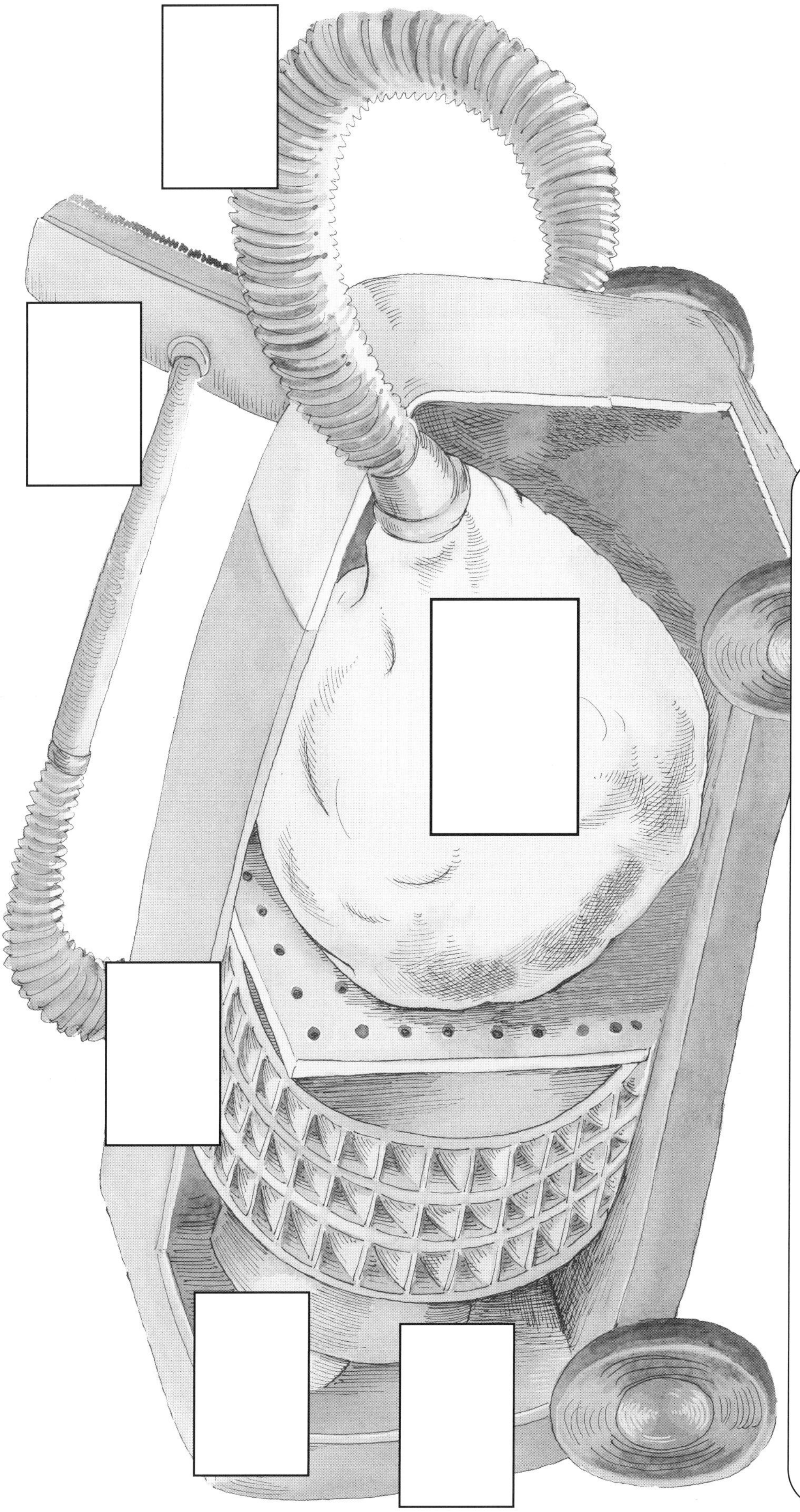

duct   electric motor   fan   dust bag   hose   head

NAME ______________________ DATE ____________

I want to explain how ______________________ works.

1 To begin with ______________________

____

This makes ______________________

because ______________________

2 After that ______________________

____

____

3 As a result, ______________________

____

4 Next ______________________

____

5 Then ______________________

____

So the ______________________

____

6 In the end ______________________

NAME ______________________________ DATE ____________

Danny has started to write down ideas for a story about an imaginary castle. He now wants to add more detail. Help him to improve his description.

1 Add words and phrases to the text below. Make the setting sound strange and sinister. Use vivid detail to help the reader 'see' the setting.

2 Join some sentences together using connectives. Try changing the order they are in.

3 Rewrite the story opening using your changes.

It was spooky. It was a cold evening. It was windy. The old castle was dark. The door was broken. There were loads of weeds growing everywhere. The leaves were blowing about. There were loads of trees. There was a bit of paper with some words on it.

NAME ______________________ DATE ____________

Setting ______________________________

What does it look like?

What can you see?

What does it smell like?

What can you hear?

Other details

NAME ______________________________ DATE ______________

Henry King

WHO CHEWED BITS OF STRING,
AND WAS EARLY CUT OFF IN DREADFUL AGONIES

The Chief Defect of Henry King
Was chewing little bits of String.
At last he swallowed some which tied
Itself in ugly Knots inside.
Physicians of the Utmost Fame
Were called at once; but when they came
They answered as they took their Fees,
"There is no Cure for this Disease.
Henry will very soon be dead."
His Parents stood about his Bed
Lamenting his Untimely Death,
When Henry, with his Latest Breath,
Cried – "Oh, my Friends, be warned by me,
That Breakfast, Dinner, Lunch and Tea
Are all the Human Frame requires . . ."
With that the Wretched Child expires.

Hilaire Belloc

NAME ______________________ DATE ______________

Make a list of all the things that are similar about the two poems.

Feature	Henry King	The Story of Augustus
Name of child		
Child's bad habit		
Tragic end		
Rhyme pattern		

NAME ______________________ DATE ____________

Planning

Name of child

Child's bad habit

What happens?

Horrible/tragic ending

Suitable adjectives

Drafting

Title of tale ______________________

Line 1 ______________________ (A)

Line 2 ______________________ (A)

Line 3 ______________________ (B)

Line 4 ______________________ (B)

Line 5 ______________________ (C)

Line 6 ______________________ (C)

NAME ____________________ DATE ____________

1 Scan the text below. Use key words to write notes about:

Pirates' lives:

Pirates' food:

2 Think of a sub-heading for the second paragraph.

Life on Board

The pirates' life was hard. They lived below deck in rat-infested quarters.

Many pirates died from horrible diseases such as yellow fever and scurvy.

They mostly ate hard-baked biscuits, fish and salted beef. When they ran out of fresh water, pirates drank beer, wine and rum.

NAME ______________________ DATE ____________

Key word quiz

1 Look at the key words below. Each set of words is about a different creature.

2 Can you guess what the creature is? Write it as a heading above the notes.

3 Write one or two sentences about the creature using the key words. Remember to use commas and full stops.

1 ______________________

eight legs spins web eats flies

____

2 ______________________

pointed nose prickles out at night

____

3 ______________________

long neck yellow/brown eats leaves

____

4 ______________________

leaves trail spiral shell four tentacles slow

____

5 ______________________

tough grey skin ivory tusks long trunk large ears

____

NAME ______________________________ DATE ______________

Main heading of Topic ______________________________

Group heading ______________________________

Make notes under each of these headings. Use key words only.

What I know already

What I need to know

What I found out

Where I found the information

NAME ______________________________ DATE ______________

Read this extract with a partner.

1 Underline all the words or phrases that are repeated.

2 What do you think happens at the end of this story?

Mr Creep the Crook

Allan Ahlberg

Page 1

Mr Creep the crook was a bad man.
Mrs Creep the crook was a bad woman.
Miss Creep and Master Creep were bad children,
and 'Growler' Creep was a bad dog.

Page 2

For some of the time Mr Creep and his family
lived in a secret den.
For the rest of the time they lived in jail.

Page 3

One day Mr Creep was sitting in his little jail-house.
He was drinking a cup of jail-house tea and eating a
piece of jail-house cake and planning how to get out.

NAME ______________________ DATE ____________

Title ______________________

Characters

Setting

What happens?

Beginning

Middle

Happy ending

NAME ______________________ DATE ____________

Title ______________________

Author(s) ______________________

Publisher ______________________

Does the cover make you want to read the book?

What questions could the book answer?

Does the book use up-to-date information?

What sources are used?

Can you find out quickly what the book is about? How?

Are there clear headings? Sub-headings?

Is there an index?

Is there a glossary?

What questions could the book answer?

What kind of illustrations are there? How do they help?

Who would enjoy it?

NAME ________________ DATE ________

Topic: Animals

Name of animal ________________

What I know already

What I need to find out

Where I might look

NAME ______________________ DATE ______________

Name of animal

Size

Skin covering

Colouring

Habitat

Food

Defence

Babies

Special features

Sources:

NAME ______________________ DATE ____________

Work with a partner. Read the poem '**I asked the little boy who cannot see**' aloud.

1. Complete these similes from the poem.

Blue is like ______________________

Pink is like ______________________

Purple is like ______________________

Yellow is like ______________________

2. Complete this sentence.

Red is like a trumpet sound because ______________________

____

3. Think of some similes of your own for these colours.

Black is like ______________________

Orange is like ______________________

Brown is like ______________________

NAME ________________________________ DATE ______________

Change the similes below by thinking of some different nouns.
The first one has been done for you.

As red as a ~~beetroot~~ postbox

As slow as a snail

As flat as a pancake

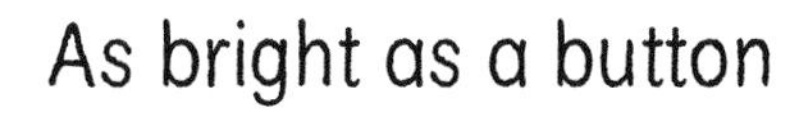

As bright as a button

As busy as a bee

As fit as a fiddle

As good as gold

As quiet as a mouse

NAME ______________________ DATE ____________

The writer of this poem

The writer of this poem

is ______________________

As strong as ______________________

As gentle as ______________________

As fast as a ______________________

As slow as ______________________

As happy as ______________________

As silly as a ______________________

As ______________________

As ______________________

As ______________________

As ______________________

NAME ______________________ DATE ____________

Scan the extract with your partner. Choose the right phrase to complete the sentences below.

1 Craig thinks Alistair is

a) cool

b) stupid

c) nasty

2 Jason asked, 'What are you?' because

a) he wants to be part of Craig's gang

b) he doesn't like Jason

c) he's scared of Craig

3 Craig says his dad calls him a tiger.

What animal would you call him? Write a sentence to say why.

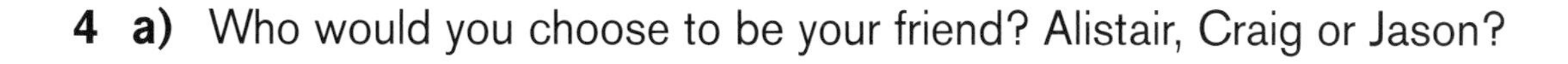

4 a) Who would you choose to be your friend? Alistair, Craig or Jason?

b) Write a sentence or two to say why.

NAME ______________________ DATE ______________

Plan the rest of the story. Try to think of some powerful verbs and adjectives to describe what the boys say and do and how they feel.

	What happens next?	What does he say?	How does he feel?
What does Craig do?			
What does Alistair do?			
What does Jason do?			

What happens in the end?

NAME ______________________ DATE ______________

What happened?	What did the character do?	What could he have done?
	Alistair	
	Jason	
	Jason	
	Next morning, Jason	

NAME ______________________________ DATE ______________

it's – shorter version of it is

<u>It's</u> very cold outside today.

its – shows that something belongs to somebody/something

The dog wagged <u>its</u> tail.

Read the sentences below and write **it's** or **its** in the gaps.

1 Craig's bike was on ______________ side.

2 The wheel was bent and ______________ spokes were broken.

3 Jason has a panda and ______________ very old. ______________ fur is worn down.

Write two sentences of your own which include **it's**.

____

____

Write two sentences of your own which include **its**.

____

____

NAME ______________________ DATE ____________

Chapter One (Introduction)

Setting

Who?

What happened?

Why?

Chapter Two (Build-up)

Dilemma

Actions taken

Consequences

Chapter Three (Climax)

New dilemma

Actions taken

Consequences

Chapter Four (Resolution)

NAME ______________________ DATE ____________

The issue we are discussing is ______________________________

____

Arguments for

Arguments against

NAME ______________________ DATE ____________

Paragraph 1: Introduce the debate

We have been debating whether ______________________

____

____

Paragraph 2: State one point of view

Some people think that ______________________

____

because ______________________ .

Also ______________________

____

Paragraph 3: State the other point of view

On the other hand, ______________________

____

because ______________________

____

Also ______________________

____

Paragraph 4: Summarise your point of view

We think that ______________________

because ______________________

NAME ______________________________ DATE ____________

Read the extract below. It comes before the extract in your book.

Sausage has dived down into the water and retrieved something from the bottom – now he has to get back to the surface.

The funny thing was, I only began to be afraid when I was going back. I suddenly thought: perhaps I've swum under-water much too far – perhaps I'll come up at the far end of the Ponds among all the fishermen and foul their lines and perhaps get a fish-hook caught in the flesh of my cheek. And all the time I was going up quite quickly, and the water was changing from brown-black to green-brown and then to bright lemonade. I could almost see the sun shining through the water, I was so near the surface. It wasn't until then that I felt really frightened: I thought I was moving much too slowly and I'd never reach the air again in time.

Never the air again ...

1 What was Sausage afraid of?

2 What was it like under the water? Underline the words and phrases that help you to imagine it.

3 Why do you think Sausage kept the tin at the end of the story?

NAME ____________ DATE ____________

Changing the ending

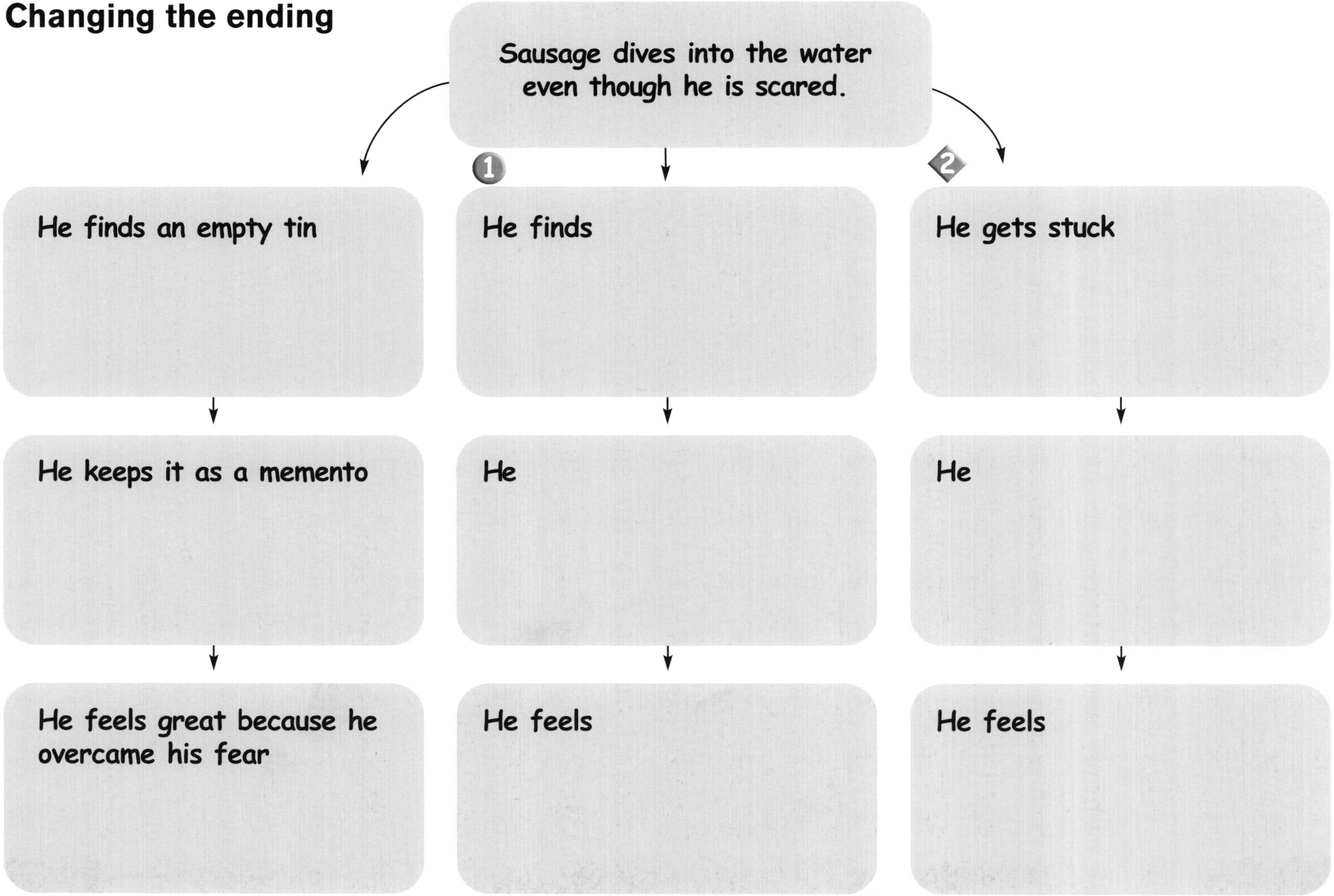

Sausage dives into the water even though he is scared.

	1	2
He finds an empty tin	He finds	He gets stuck
He keeps it as a memento	He	He
He feels great because he overcame his fear	He feels	He feels

NAME ____________________ DATE ____________

Because it wasn't a brick. It was just about the size and shape of one, but it was a ____________________

It was all ____________________

____________________ from being in the pond. Inside it there was ____________________

____

It was ____________________

____

It must have come from ____________________

____

Sausage ____________________

____

He took it home and ____________________

____

He felt ____________________

____

NAME ______________________________ DATE ____________

Look at the features on the chart. Put a tick if the advert uses the feature. Put a cross if it does not.

	Advert for ice cream 1	Advert for ice cream 2
Language		
catchy phrases		
exaggerated		
alliteration		
big promises		
'new'		
'special offer'		
free gifts		
something for everyone		
Layout		
big lettering		
different font styles		
star shapes, bubbles etc		
bright colours		

NAME ______________________ DATE ____________

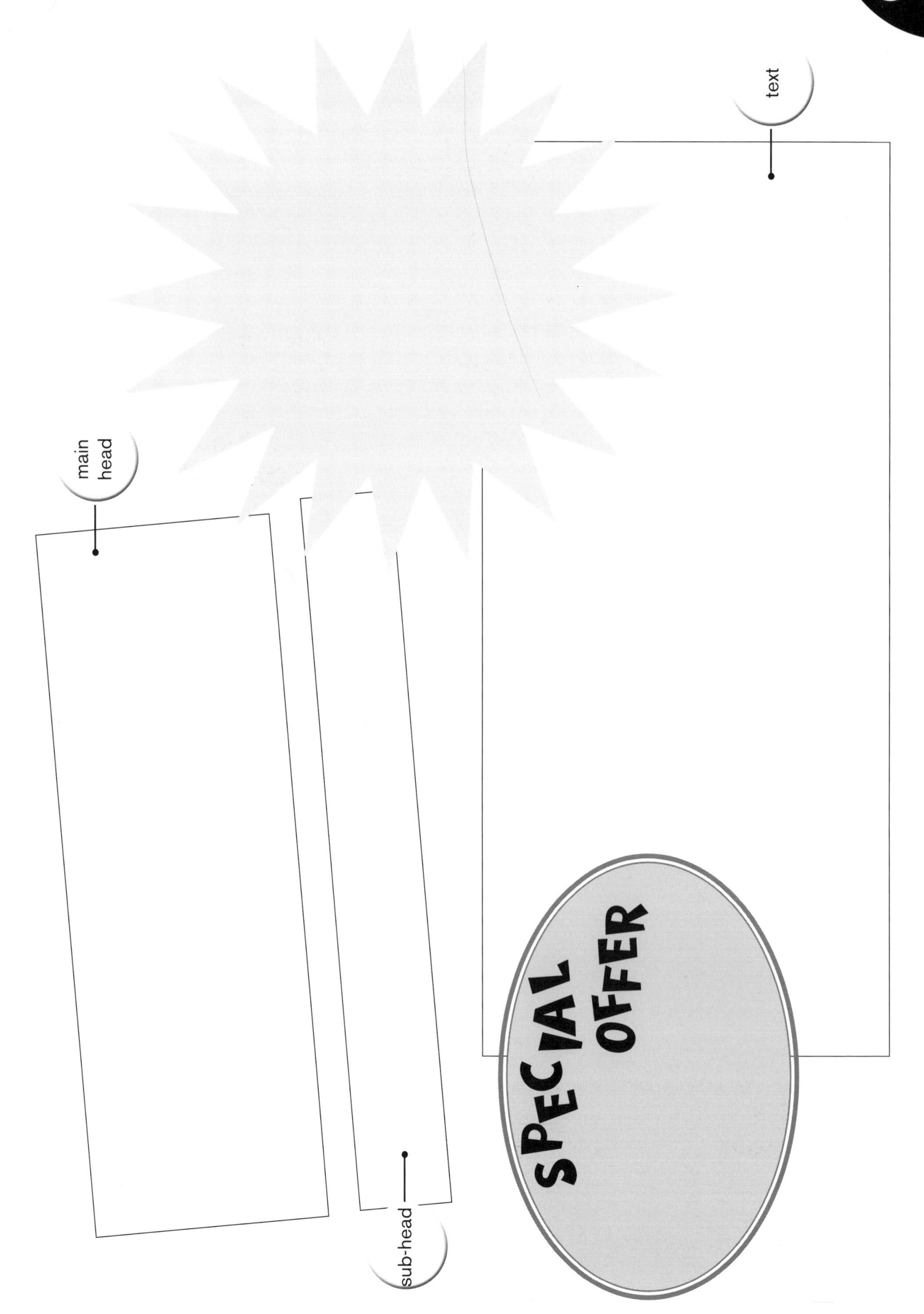

NAME ____________________ DATE __________

Read through the poem '**Childhood Tracks**' again.
List the senses James Berry describes on the senses web below.
Some examples have been done for you.

sweaty padding lifted
off a donkey's back

smelling

crisp fried fish

tasting

goats in shade
cud-chewing

seeing

dawn-crowing cocks

hearing

the soft fur
of the donkey

touching

NAME ______________________ DATE ____________

Home from School

What do you see, hear, smell, taste and touch in the first half hour after you get home from school? Make notes below.

NAME ______________________________ DATE ______________

Home from School

Seeing

Hearing

Smelling

Tasting

Touching

NAME ______________________ DATE ____________

Read Mrs Lacey's letter.

1 Underline the arguments she uses to try and keep Mark off school.

2 Complete the sentences below.

Dear Mr Jenkins,

I am writing to ask if I could possibly keep Mark off school next week because we have the chance to take a wonderful holiday in Spain.

I think it's very important to learn about the world by seeing it. I'll make Mark take some school work. I'm sure he'll benefit from all the new experiences.

I do hope you will agree to let him go. I know how important it is to attend school regularly but this is a chance in a lifetime.

Yours sincerely

Angela Lacey

1 Mrs Lacey's most convincing argument is ______________________

____

because ______________________________________

____

2 Mrs Lacey's weakest argument is ______________________

____

because ______________________________________

____

NAME ________________________________ DATE ______________

Dear

I am writing to ask if ______________________________________

____

There are several reasons why I think ______________________

____

The first is that ____

____

Another reason is that ______________________________________

____

Lastly, ____

____

I'm sure you will agree that ________________________________

____

____

Yours sincerely/faithfully

NAME ______________________ DATE ____________

Write some more lines for this skipping rhyme.
Think of action words that rhyme with the numbers.
Think of the actions that could go with each line.

Oliver-Oliver-Oliver Twist

Bet you a penny you can't do this:

Number one – touch your tongue

Number two – touch your shoe

Number three – touch your knee

Number four – ______________________

Number five – ______________________

Number six – ______________________

Number seven – ______________________

Number eight – ______________________

Number nine – ______________________

Number ten – ______________________

NAME ____________________ DATE ____________

Finish the sentences

The first book I remember reading is ____________________

The best book I've read this term is ____________________

My favourite place for reading is ____________________

My favourite time for reading is ____________________

For me, the three most important things which make a good story are:

-
-
-

Three things I hate:

-
-
-

NAME ______________________ DATE ____________

What I like

What makes a good story for me is:

What I don't like

Three things I don't like in stories:

NAME ______________________ DATE ____________

PRESENTATION NOTES

Name of author

Publisher

Titles

What makes this author special?

Who would enjoy these books?

Favourite characters

Favourite scenes

Favourite quotes

PROMPT CHART 1

Response Partner Rules

Partner 1

Read your work aloud.

Partner 2

Listen carefully.

Both of you

Don't worry too much about punctuation or spelling.

Partner 2

Pick out some bits you like.

✸

Say what is good about them.

✸

Pick out some bits you want to improve.

✸

Pick out anything you don't understand.

✸

Is it too long or too short?

Partner 1

If you want to, ask your partner to help you with some more ideas.

NOW SWAP ROLES

PROMPT CHART 2

Planning a Story

Ask yourself:

Who are the main characters?

♦

What are they like?

♦

Where is it set?

♦

When is it set?

♦

Why do things happen?

♦

How do they happen?

♦

What happens in the end?

Stages of a story

Introduction

♦

Build up

♦

Problem

♦

Climax

♦

Resolution

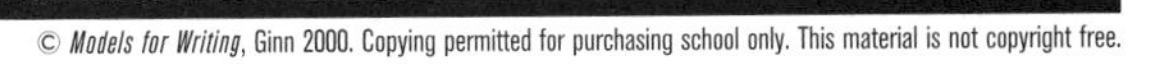

PROMPT CHART 3

Descriptive Writing and Building Tension

Use all your senses.

❊

Use short sentences.

❊

Include some short paragraphs.

❊

Ask questions.

❊

Use similes.

❊

Give precise details.

❊

Create a mystery.

❊

Help the reader to imagine how you
or your character feels.

Writing Poetry

Think hard about what you are describing.

Use all your senses: see, hear, smell, taste, touch.

Make sure you have exactly the right word.

Cut out any words you don't need.

Start a new line when you want to pause.

PROMPT CHART 5

Information Texts

Plan

Brainstorm what you know already.

Group your ideas under headings.

Decide on the sub-headings.

What do you need to find out?

Research

Make notes:
key words only

don't write sentences

make a note of your sources

Write

Begin with an introduction.

Write short, clear sentences.

End with a summary.

Use illustrations or diagrams if they will make things clearer.

Explanation

Say what happens.

■

Say how or why it happens.

Introduce the subject.

■

Use a sequence of steps.

■

Use the present tense.

■

Use words like *then* *next* *after* to put things in order.

■

Use words like *because* *therefore* *so* to explain why.

Make your explanation easy to follow by using:

numbered points

■

labelled diagrams or drawings

■

short sentences

■

short paragraphs

PROMPT CHART 7

Stories for Younger Children

Use:

simple words

not too many words on each page

repeated words

short sentences

pictures on every page

not too scary

happy ending

PROMPT CHART 8

Presenting a Point of View

Say what you think.

Explain why you think that.

Use examples to back up your argument.

Show the arguments for both sides.

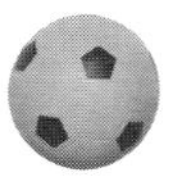

Sum up by recapping what you think.

Use polite, formal language.

Persuasive Features of Adverts, Posters, etc

CATCHY PHRASES.

•

NOT TOO MANY WORDS.

•

EXAGGERATION.

•

ALLITERATION.

USE:

EYE-CATCHING LAYOUT

BIG LETTERING

different fonts

BRIGHT COLOURS

PROMPT CHART 10

Persuasive Letters

Be polite.

Tell the reader what you want them to do and why.

Use good arguments.

Say things the reader will want to hear.

Make it sound like a good idea for the reader as well as for you!

Use connectives to join your sentences.

OHT Correlation Chart

In recognition of the fact that not all schools are equipped with the facilities for using overhead transparencies, we have supplied here as additional photocopiable sheets, any OHTs which do not appear elsewhere, either as text in the Pupil's Book or PCMs.

Below is a correlation chart, which will help you to match the OHT reference in the Teacher's Book to the appropriate Pupil's Book extract, PCM or additional photocopiable sheet.

UNIT	OHT reference from Teacher's Book	Cross reference to appropriate PCM, Pupil's Book page or additional photocopiable sheet
1	OHT 1	Pupil's Book pages 4–5
1	OHT 2	PCM 4
2	OHT 3	PCM 6
3	OHT 4	Provided here as a photocopiable sheet
4	OHT 5	Pupil's Book page 10
4	OHT 6	Provided here as a photocopiable sheet
5	OHT 7	Provided here as a photocopiable sheet
5	OHT 8	PCM 14
7	OHT 9	Pupil's Book page 17
7	OHT 10	PCM 21
8	OHT 11	PCM 23
9	OHT 12	Pupil's Book page 22
9	OHT 13	PCM 24
10	OHT 14	Pupil's Book page 24
10	OHT 15	Provided here as a photocopiable sheet
11	OHT 16	Pupil's Book pages 26–27 (map only)
12	OHT	17 Pupil's Book pages 29–30 (lines 1–24)
12	OHT 18	Provided here as a photocopiable sheet
13	OHT 19	PCM 35
14	OHT 20	Pupil's Book pages 35–36 (lines xx–xx)
14	OHT 21	Provided here as a photocopiable sheet
15	OHT 22	PCM 38
15	OHT 23	PCM 40
16	OHT 24	Provided here as a photocopiable sheet
16	OHT 25	Brainstorm on a flipchart, or use PCM 43
17	OHT 26	Provided here as a photocopiable sheet
17	OHT 27	PCM 45
18	OHT 28	PCM 46
20	OHT 29	Pupil's Book page 48 – 'The writer of this poem'
20	OHT 30	PCM 51
23	OHT 31	PCM 56
24	OHT 32	Pupil's Book page 58
24	OHT 33	PCM 58
25	OHT 34	Provided here as a photocopiable sheet
26	OHT 35	PCM 63
27	OHT 36	Pupil's Book page 64 (first 3 verses)
27	OHT 37	Use flipchart with headings: **Hearing Smelling**
28	OHT 38	PCM 68
30	OHT 39	Pupil's Book page 70
30	OHT 40	PCM 72

John's Plan

❶ **John's teacher asked everyone to think about an object and to write a story about it.**

❷ **Working with his partner, John brainstormed some ideas about an old pair of shoes. He used a spider diagram to help him. He circled his best ideas.**

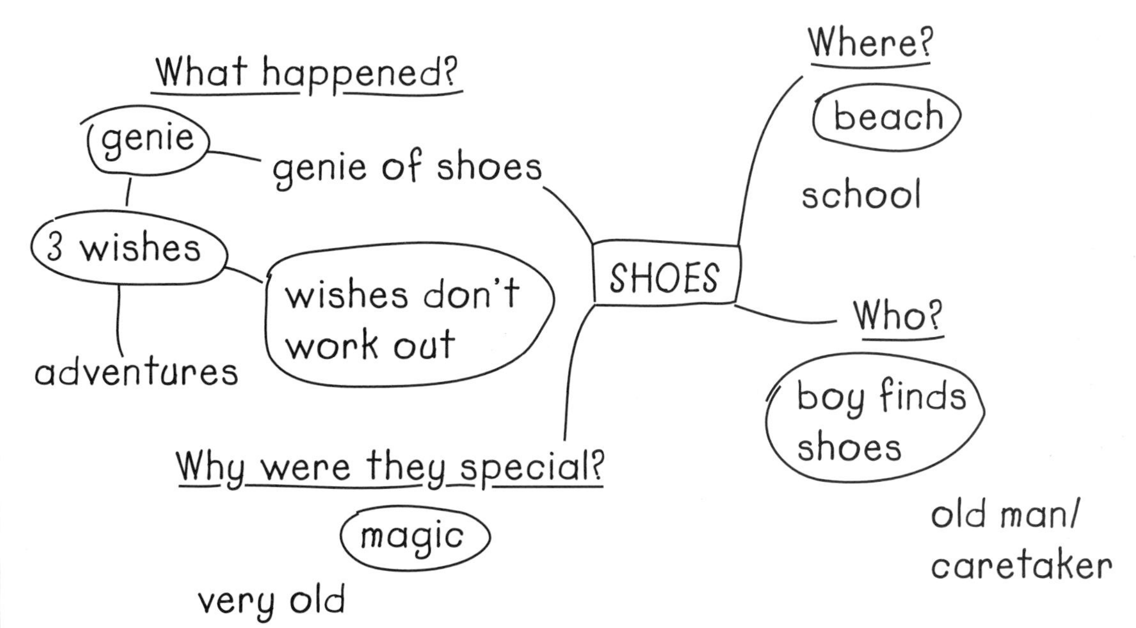

❸ **John then planned his story.**

Introduction	find shoes
Build-up	genie appears
Climax	3 wishes
Resolution	genie vanishes normal life

Chapter 2

On a hill above the valley there was a wood.

In the wood there was a huge tree.

Under the tree there was a hole.

In the hole lived Mr Fox and Mrs Fox and their four small foxes.

Every evening as soon as it got dark, Mr Fox would say to Mrs Fox, 'Well, my darling, what shall it be this time? A plump chicken from Boggis? A duck or a goose from Bunce? Or a nice turkey from Bean?' And when Mrs Fox had told him what she wanted, Mr Fox would creep down into the darkness of the night and help himself.

Boggis and Bunce and Bean knew very well what was going on, and it made them wild with rage ...

'Dang and blast that lousy beast!' cried Boggis.

'I'd like to rip his guts out!' said Bunce.

'He must be killed!' cried Bean.

'But how?' said Boggis. 'How on earth can we watch the blighter?'

Bean picked his nose delicately with a long finger. 'I have a plan,' he said.

'You've never had a decent plan yet,' said Bunce.

'Shut up and listen,' said Bean. 'Tomorrow night we will all hide just outside the hole where the fox lives. We will wait there until he comes out. Then ... *Bang! Bang-bang-bang.*'

Scene:

On one side of the stage ______________________________

______________________________ *and on the other side*

____

MR FOX [____________________]: ______________________________

____

____

MRS FOX: ______________________________

[*Mr Fox crept* ______________________________]

A HAT TRICK OF BREAK-INS

by Charles Hague

Ashwood School has had a triple break-in, and three items of value were stolen.

The robberies took place on November 5th, 8th and 9th; twice in the nursery and once in the headteacher's office. Thieves took a stereo, fax machine, video and lap-top computer. The first two items were stolen from the nursery, and the lap-top computer from the headteacher's office.

Police and the school have no idea who carried out the robberies. The police took fingerprints, and are still baffled.

The robbers entered using a fire-exit and a window. They used a drain pipe to smash the window. Police have found no evidence of weapons or damage, apart from the window and door. The school was empty at the time of the break-ins, and nobody reported hearing the alarm.

"We haven't had any break-ins for a while," said Mr Brown, the caretaker of Ashwood school. He thinks that people on the street ignored the alarm, because the fireworks could have set it off. Mr Brown didn't know until he opened up in the morning. He told our reporter, "In my opinion, they knew what they were looking for. They probably knew the school."

Police think that the robbers were, 'straight in and straight out'. They said, "We think they struck on the 5th, because of fireworks, so they could fool the alarm system."

If you have further information contact 01709 710847

e-mail: www.ashwood.co.uk

Charles, age 10

MOODS

ANIMALS

VERBS and ADVERBS

I have a ______________________ in me

[verb] ______________ ing [adverb] ______________ ly

[adverb] ______________ ly [verb] ______________ ing

[adverb] ______________ [verb] ______________

[verb] ______________ [adverb] ______________

[how do people react?] ______________________________

____

[how does your animal feel about this?] ________________

____

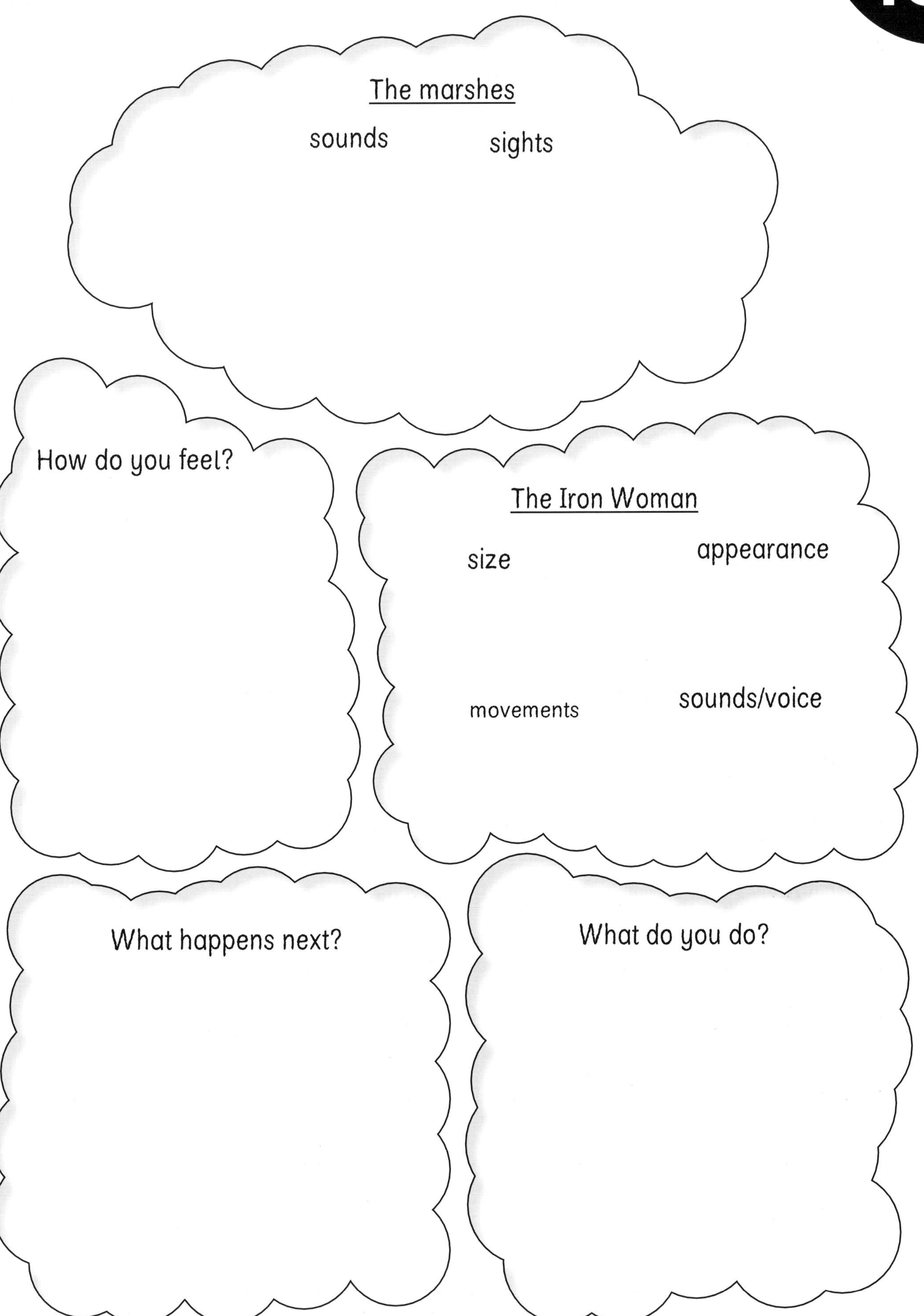
The marshes
sounds
sights
How do you feel?
The Iron Woman
size
appearance
movements
sounds/voice
What happens next?
What do you do?

Setting ____

Danny has started to write down ideas for a story about an imaginary castle. He now wants to add more detail. Help him to improve his description.

It was spooky. It was a cold evening. It was windy. The old castle was dark. The door was broken. There were loads of weeds growing everywhere. The leaves were blowing about. There were loads of trees. There was a bit of paper with some words on it.

Pirates

Ever since ships have carried cargo, pirates have attacked them to steal.

In the 1600s and early 1700s, thousands of ships were carrying valuable cargoes back to Europe. These large, slow ships were easy targets for pirates. They attacked ships full of gold from South America.

Pirate ships

Pirates often stole their ships. These were small, fast and armed with large cannon and many smaller guns.

The crew

A pirate crew was a mixed bunch. Some were criminals who had run away to sea. Others were sailors taken from captured ships and forced into piracy. Some pirates were women, who fought fearlessly with men.

When they plundered a ship, each member of the crew was given a share of the clothes, jewels and money stolen from the passengers.

Mrs Wobble the Waitress

Mrs Wobble was a waitress.
She liked her work.
The customers liked her.
The only trouble was – she wobbled.

1

One day Mrs Wobble wobbled
with a bowl of soup.
The soup landed on a
customer's dog.
Mrs Wobble got told off.

2

The next day Mrs Wobble wobbled
with a roast chicken.
The roast chicken landed
on a customer's head.
Mrs Wobble got told off again.

3

The next day Mrs Wobble wobbled
with a plate of jelly.
The jelly landed on the
manager's head.
Mrs Wobble got the sack.

Allan Ahlberg

4

Paragraph 1

Because it wasn't a brick. It was just about the size and shape of one, but it was a

Paragraph 2

What does he do with it?

How does he feel?

How does it end?

Home from School